My name is LOLA

Text and Photographs by Marcia Goldman

This is me when I was little.

I love to have
my belly rubbed,

and I love to give kisses.

Eating is my favorite activity,

**especially when I
get treats.**

Getting brushed is not
my favorite activity!

I love to go outside and
sniff the air

or sniff the flowers
in the garden.

Sometimes I like to lie
in the sun,

and when it gets too hot, I lie in the shade.

I have two cat friends.
This is Isabel,

and this is Gus.

**When I see
Gus outside,**

I jump through my
dog door,

so we can
play together.

When my family is gone, I watch through the window.

Or I wait by the door,

and dance for joy when they come home!

When I hear "let's go,"
my ears perk up.

I jump right into the car,
and I am ready to go.

I wonder where
we are going?

Maybe we are going to visit my friend, Abbie.

My favorite adventure is going to the pet store.

I wonder what we are
going to buy?

When we are all done, the nice lady gives me a treat.

But wherever we go, I am always happy to be back home!

Lola is a five-pound Yorkshire terrier who lives in California with her adoring owners and her pet cat. She is a proud certified therapy dog who makes weekly visits to elderly care centers, book stores, and classrooms. She happily participated in the making of this book and hopes you enjoy reading it.

Edwards Brothers, Inc.
Thorofare, NJ USA
October 4, 2011